D1178382

Natural Mechanical

NATURAL MECHANICAL

*being a rendering
of the true life stories of
Iain Seoras Rockcliffe*

J. O. Morgan

(B *editions*

These stories are to
Lisa & Seoras

First printed in 2008 by Reefort
This edition published in 2009
by CB editions
146 Percy Road London W12 9QL
www.cbeditions.com

Printed in England by Primary Colours, London W3 8DH

ISBN 978–0–9557285–9–4

Apologia

That the episodes presented here, though they do not appear in their exact chronology, are placed in a specific order and should be read, in the first instance, in that order.

That though the language of the Inner Hebrides at the time in which these events take place was primarily Gaelic, the language given here is primarily English; neither has the vernacular been used in the representation of speech.

That though the narrative is poetic in form and structure, the work as a whole is presented primarily as a biographical sketch, with the manner of its presentation secondary to that aspect.

That though the events described are all perfectly true and unembellished, the work as a whole has been approached by the author as a work of fiction.

Thanks

to Iain – that is: Rocky
whose life, at least in part, this work will show.

See this boy – this Rocky.

At three years: the back door opened.
Out he goes. Prompted. Prodded. Pushed.
Squat body. Crew-cut. Short trousers. Green vest.
Little fists clenched into little pink rocks.

He'll be a hardy wee bugger this one.

His father. Nailing the child's bedroom window open.
Four inch gap. Forever. No curtain.

The third of three children; the Benjamin.
Following the second sister by five years.
No more to come after.

He's been up and running
for half his whole life.

His mother. Allowing the wind to slam shut the door.

Let him play out where my legs
are least likely to find him.

And if he doesn't come back when called
The father again:
   then it'll be the webbing belt.
his Victorian ideals coming fifty years too late.

And this boy – this Rocky – takes to it, quick.
An t-Eilean Sgitheanach. The Wingéd Isle. Isle of Skye. His.

And when they later call his name
over wind, over heath, over burn, over bog

he doesn't hear, and he doesn't come.

At home it's the Gaelic that rolls from his tongue.
Although he need not speak it very much.

The language of streams, of rock, of wood –
of nettles, as taught by their stings:
that handled right can make a three-fold cord
yet firm enough to catch a full-grown hare
and hold it fast – is much more to his liking.

The tongue of the classroom is English.

   Read the words as you've been taught,
   or weren't you even listening.

As in a dream the letters stay as letters.
They are glue. Have no perspective depth.
Their shapes mean nothing other than their shapes.
Have no relevance to sound, to throat. Un-word-like.

   We know that you're not stupid.
   A stupid child can't hook a fish by hand.
   Your sisters aren't stupid.

Suspicions are he might not be all there. Close.
Frustrated taunting blinds them to the link.

So when he shakes his head and does not speak
the teacher makes him wear a tall white hat
then stands him by the back wall of her class
– a remedy that's always worked before.

Beneath the narrow cone the boy
thinks hard on what he has or has not done.

His own solution: NOT TO GO TO SCHOOL.

His teaching to be gathered from the earth.
From scrub and thicket: *profit*, never dearth.

'I used to say he'd end up
living in a dunce's house.
Shock tactics. And of course they worked.
Just look at what my boy's achieved.

Look where he's been.
Look at his hands.
Wash off the oil, dear,
before you come in.'

A roundtrip ticket for the longnose bus: 1s. 6d.

The driver knows him well enough,
charges nothing extra for his dog;
allows the boy to help deliver post.

Back seat. Corner seat. His seat.
Dog Kim lying quiet at his feet.

And as they walk the path up to the school,
him in his secondhand McKinnon kilt,
Kim, in brown, trots noiselessly behind.

And as they reach the gate they split.
No word. No sign. The dog just goes;
out of sight around the building's walls.

Marked present on the register, the boy
at the first opportunity slips out the back.

There: his dog.
Single pat.
They go.

Later on the bus,
in quite a different region of the isle:

> *Shouldn't you be at school, Rocky.*
> *Aye, my mother kens well where I am.*

No more is said.

His grandma has a gramophone.
A rare thing. A beautiful thing.
Cased in solid oak. High polish.
Its wood from a 600-year-old tree;
gives a finer gold-flecked grain;
condenses the tone.

Beneath the brown-topped turntable
– rubber-matted, free of dust –
its internal trumpet. Extending downward.
At most times unseen within the square body.

Volume control is by way of its two front doors.
For a church hall, say, the doors can be left wide.
There, direct from the brass-mouthed gape, the sound
escapes freely, fills the hall, bounces, doubles.

At home: the doors kept closed. Thin music
is made to pass through the yellow oak casing,
picks up something from the wood, its density, its age,
carries it, piggy-backed, resonating into small space.

The gramophone's *rent-to-buy* price: £4 3s. 2d.

She pays a shilling a week, and when there are guests
only Rocky is permitted to operate the mechanisms:
palms cupping the thick black edges of a disc,
the silver node of the spindle, untouched;
his delicate drop – needle to groove;
stands military as the music plays.

His grandfather is a drinking man.
One day the alcohol will kill him.

He takes the boy to a fête in a near town. Four-mile walk.
The gramophone: carried in the bowl of a wheelbarrow.
A stained candlewick blanket, doubled over, wraps it,
protects it, from the other oddments carried alongside:
    a 2½-foot-diameter aluminium plate,
    a lightweight collapsible table frame,
    a small gas canister with burner & pipe,
    a roll of fine wire meshing – medium gauge.

And in procession, bringing up the rear:
three Khaki Campbell ducks;
sleek-headed, mottled plumage;
evenly spaced along a length of string, a single loop
fixed loose about each of their delicate throats.

At the fête, within the tent he's been assigned,
Rocky plays the records he has brought:
    Dvořák's 'NEW WORLD' SYMPHONY,
    3 SUITES FROM ROMEO & JULIET,
    that sort of thing;
is careful with each – expensive plastic at 3s. 6d.,
available only by order through mainland post.

Outside the tent, this is the music passers-by hear
– punctuated by the occasional quack.

Inside they see: the boy, the gramophone, the ducks;
the grandfather being by this time nowhere present.

The ducks are set forward, on a table, on a metal plate,
with an old sheet draped down over the table's front,
with a high dome of wire mesh neatly caging the ducks.

The spectators are bemused at the scene
– but the music is good, so they stay.

And when enough have gathered,
and when it looks as though they might soon leave,
the music stops, abrupt, as Rocky takes the record off –
only to replace it with Herb Miller's IN THE MOOD.

Quick change. Slick. Itself a joy to watch – to some extent.
The gramophone's doors flicked wide.

And as the solo saxophone starts off its thirteen beats,
the boy dips down behind the ducks
and twists the bunsen-burner's neck
from yellow flame to blue.

His timing is immaculate.

Just as the horns and trumpets join the song,
and in so doing hold the many listeners to the tent,
so the plate, one yard above the burner, grows hot.

And that is when the ducks begin to dance.

> Their flat feet, jagged lifting,
> shifting weight, to cool
> their bare skin for that moment
> in the air, back down,
> and lift again, their bobbing
> careful shuffle, seeking out
> that perfect spot, the heat
> not hot enough to burn,
> but never in their dancing
> do they make a sound.

The takings for the day are reasonable,
are worthy of the effort of the trip.

As they trudge home along the narrow road
it's the boy that guides the balance of the barrow.

Every few hundred yards he has to rest,
just for a second or two, just from the weight of it.
More often he is required to guide
his grandfather's heavy drunken stagger;
with simply worded directions saves him
time and again from falling in the ditch.

The ducks follow close behind.
Looped into their single length of string.
Quacking happy at the cool of the road in the evening;
sleek-headed, bright-eyed
– occasional shake of a tail.

'She was a fine woman that granny of his,
a hardy woman – never sat on a chair.

Two beer crates, a thick plank of wood
joining the two – with her on top.

And that's where she'd sit, before the fire,
bolt upright – weaving a stocking.

The boy built a cabinet for her new television;
a tall sturdy square thing it was,
with space below for groceries and such.

By then of course she couldn't hear a thing.
But she could lip-read well enough.
That's why she wanted the television:
the gramophone was no use to her any more.'

Round most of the houses on Skye: a croft.
Little patches of farmable land, but with access
to areas outwith their ownership; grazeable hillsides,
communal; for those who have cattle or sheep –
though not all of the crofters have cattle or sheep.

The produce is small; a little for trade,
a share for the crofters themselves;
and rabbits, many hundreds of thousands of rabbits,
them too, they each take a share.

Not that the rabbits' cut comes from the beasts,
but grasses thin quick under so many mouths.

As such the crofters, the men,
the workers of the run-rig system,
on the slopes counting stock,
greasing the handplough's blade,
cold-calving in the long grass by the burn;
they none of them mind to see the boy
out on his rounds, crossing unlined borders,
checking and setting his snares with such care.

They watch him, they pause, and they watch, and
unsmiling they smile to be rid of a few more rabbits.

He uses nettles for his string,
can't recall where he learned it, just strips
all the leaves from the stalk as he walks
head stooped, eyes out wide, careful trudge;
strips the stalk without looking, no stings,
then splits it, his thumbnail – right down its long length,
twice pares it, then braids the three strands,
uneven, not caring, not watching,
but watching the line of the barbed-wire fence
or the hedge or the wall or the grass
for tell-tale holes, then he stops.

Not easy to trick a creature on its doorstep.

And rabbits are cautious by nature,
not just by their wraparound eyes,
their long whiskers go always before them
and if one tip touches something uncertain,
be it wire or plastic, leather or bone,
whatever disturbs them, so they will draw back,
and gently lollop down a different route.

Which is why the boy uses nettle-string for his snares.

He sets them: the hole, the stake, the loop, the noose,
then goes on his way,
to check another he has set some time before.

He can't set too many at once,
for he can't tell for sure when he'll be coming back,
and a maggoty rabbit is no good for anything,
merely a shameful waste.

He never does see the catch itself;
the final cautious sniff, the forward hop,
the silent slide of the knot down the green nettle-string,
the hollow deepening round the tawny fur.

A gentle tug at first, the rabbit
has felt such before, is unconcerned, hops on.

Then the jerk.
Then the dance:
the fight to draw breath, the air
free-drifting all around – that won't go in.

He never hears the piercing cry,
the cold unearthly squeal, nor sees
the other rabbits scarper in alarm.

The closest he comes is finding one just newly dead.

Still warm.
Wet grass, no sun – so it couldn't be that.
Still limp as he lifts it.
Single ear-twitch as the string is loosed, drawn off.
Still a glimmer in the liquid of its simple eye.
One spot of unclotted blood on its lip.

He lifts it. Inspects it briefly –
for beetles, for worms, for any unwanted imperfection.
Then lowers it into his schoolbag,
a small hessian sack, no books,
and closes the flap.

Often on his rounds a snare lies empty.
And he dismantles and relocates it.

Less often he finds no snare at all.
Then he curses the crofters – but thinks not
how he was the thief before they were.

On his way to the butcher's he chances the bus.

With three dead in his bag he knows
he's not allowed, but it's a shame
having to waste half a ticket he's already paid for.

Stepping up he holds the ticket high,
the driver smiles and calmly shakes his head,
and Rocky shrugs and off he gets.

Soon after, it begins to rain.

Isle of Skye. The Wingéd Isle.
An t-Eilean Sgitheanach. His.

Its peaks.
Its mists.
Its creatures.
Its breath.

And in the schoolhouse
the boy with the permanent frown is learning
about the Tudors.

His father: ex-Naval.
Strong in his smallness, his roundness
– compacted. With anvils for arms.

Sees himself in his son, but won't say.
The stature. The steel.

Now working for the AA as patrolman.
His bike and his sidecar: his method –
needing to find first a breakdown in order to fix it,
will happen upon maybe two in a day.

At just under £4 in wages per week
– it isn't so bad.
Enough for a family of five.

He can make it right round the island
in two and a half hours. And never
will push to make it in less.

But it's down to the Kyle to be ferried
across to the mainland each morning
that makes his employment worthwhile.

Not much traffic to speak of on Skye. Not for now.

And sometimes, just sometimes, when on his way home,
he picks out the shape of the boy through the dusk,
on the road, in a field, up a tree –
it matters not which, it's the shape that he knows,
recognises himself, but won't say.

When the beam of his headlamp has marked him for sure,
and above the throb of the engine a name has been called,
home they both go, each at the end of their rounds.

One straddling the bike as before,
the other in miniature gripping the rim of the car,
fierce-eyed, fierce teeth,
in the face of the wind that they make.

At home it's the belt: a matter of course;
though no word is spoken
and nothing is taken away.

'It was only natural to be worried –
when night came on and still he didn't show.
At least that's how it was at first.

After a while we tired of calling,
unknowing of how many mountains
divided our lips from his ears.

Instead we'd search the cloudmass for a gap,
and think how that same starlight fell on him.
And tell ourselves: he'll come home when he's hungry.'

Though hard to get at, crows' eggs are the best.

Worth every scratch every bruise every poke in the eye
from all those climbs that end in finding
nothing but an empty nest
– just for the few that do not.

And the grin he can't hold back
when the small thickness of his fingers held up high
close unseen upon such delicacies.

Their perfect curve. Their marbled sheen. Their:
still-warm-from-a-mother-having-fled-the-nest-in-fright.

The climb down: calmed and steadied
by his rapt anticipation.

Broken open at the bubble-end
his small pink tongue inserted
spoons the yellow from the clear
drawn back whole into his mouth
the teeth to split the sac and spill the cream,
the syrup follows after.

In just one egg: all patience needs
to build a baby crow, then crack the shell.

But hand and tooth and belly stopped the clock.

Apart from the brown plank floor
– that never knew a carpet, nor a rug –
the colours of his bedroom: yellow, white, black.

A neat job – skirting, walls and door.
As hard-wearing as the triplecoat
applied to locomotives, and as bright.

The only paint his father could get cheap
– from work.

The boy is never in it enough to care.

But Kim's first night in that small square of space
fills him and then the house with howls.

The dog's unrest not at the decoration.
Nor at the draught from windows that don't close.
Uncertainty of his new situation is enough.

After sleeping the rest of the night downstairs,
and a full day's explaining from his new surround,
he doesn't do it again, nor anything as bad.

Sheepdog size.
Sheepdog ears.
Sheepdog face.
Sheepdog tail.
But not a sheepdog.
Wrong colour for a start.

He never worries sheep.
Has not been trained.
Doesn't need it.
He and his young master get on by mutual agreement
– one does what the other says.

The only thing he is known for
outwith his exemplary obedience
is a tendency to camp out on the doorstep
of any frisky bitch whose scent he's caught.

One day he will be shot and killed
for nothing more nor less than this.

When off to set snares
or lay out lines for trout,
it's best to go alone.
For others would only be

> *What you doing with that then, Rocky?*
> *Why does it no know it's there, Rocky?*
> *How say we jam this down its hole, Rocky.*

tramping the grass to a muddy mush
giving a warren good cause to pack its bags

> *You must have hands of pink leather.*
> *Given I did that, it'd jag me like a jellyfish.*

dunking sweaty fingers into freshwater to cool
scaring a dozen downstream noses with soluble stench.

And yet, on occasion, when it chances
that he has no traps to check or set,
he walks the half mile to his nearest neighbours.

Though respectfully polite to Mrs Ogilvie
she yet views him with suspicion, but having
for the time being no good reason to say no,
releases her three at his request.

Harry: the eldest – older than him by a year.
Stuart: three-year gap – will give a go at anything they say.
William: nappied – his smallness often proving useful.

There is a sister too: Sheena;
not included in their treks;
suits her well enough.

A family that's better off than most, all things considered.
Later it transpires the father is a gambling man.
For him, at least, the risking pays out well.
Has a car – an island rarity.

But William has a big-wheeled iron-sprung pram.
And steering that with four small boys aboard,
asks less of skill than prayer for clear roads.

His latest method: to listen with all his might
to the murmurs of his teacher as
she chalks her line of words on to the board.

If confident enough he's heard aright
it's his hand goes up first – slow lift.
She's only too delighted, picks him quick.

His carefully strained recital,
eyes fitting length of line
to mentally approximated time.

Some mistakes deliberate, some unavoidable,
some making no logical sense at all, and yet
she never cottons to his little scam, but then
it is done for his own peace of mind, not for her.

'The problem is he never really tried.
Oh yes, if we'd known then what we know now,
we'd have made that special effort for his need.

But would the extra tutelage have helped?
with him so strange and reticent a boy?
Apologies won't make amends – what could I do?

I'm sorry for the inkwells though, a shame
that on top of everything he had to be left-handed.
By the time we got slates – the damage was done.'

The butcher: his scrutiny of the rabbits,
three laid out long upon his counter,
ungutted, just as he likes them. Fresh.
Cannot deny their cleanliness. Impressed.

> *I'll give you three and six for all.*
> *Though rightly the end one's a leveret.*
> *You weren't to know. It'll taste the same.*

Rocky knows just fine. Knows too his place,
says nothing in return. Takes the money and goes.

Hot day. Bright sun.
Fine blue, brushed white: the sky above the isle.
And when a breath of air does blow
it touches dry upon the cheek. Moves on.

Here, slowly through such heat, four small boys trudge.

Their leader – not the eldest – sets the path;
has chosen now to check some lines he set;
the others follow diligently after.

Thin shirts cling to pink skin.

They avoid the coolness of woods
for fear of biting flies housed under trees,
unable to hold their breath for long on such a day.

On reaching the spot all lines lie untouched,
with brass hooks free and glinting in the current
bobbing taut against the pull of the burn's clear flow.
And yet the burn itself is a relief.
Hands become cups. Faces submerge.
Shirts are stripped and soaked and put back on.

But water alone will not suffice, and so
they are led on just a little further, until
ahead they see the stone walls of the convent.

Big and square. Set on high ground
with sloping gardens, down and wide, away.

Enclosed.

Within: THE SISTERS OF THE POOR.
Has housed the order for 300 years.
Their mission never changing
nor the building's simple elegance of stone.

> *Have you ever heard the screams?*

Heads shake.

> *Poor girls go in big and come out thin.*
> *And carry nothing in their arms.*

Some frowns.

> *I heard that service was reserved*
> *for the nuns themselves, by need.*
> *Sisters, stupid. No men in there.*
> *Aye, but surely, monks may come and go.*

They laugh.

Then Rocky, mind on other matters,
eyes fixed on the convent all the while, speaks up.

> *There's foxes in these parts.*
> *Maybe all that anybody ever heard*
> *was vixens crying in the night.*

The others shrug.
The truth irrelevant in such a heat.

Midday. The convent quiet. All nuns inside.

No sign of habit, brown and white,
at window or high parapet;
nor can a soul be seen out strolling
through the landscape of the gardens,
wide and long and low
its many quarters and its crops,
in gentle admiration of their self-sufficiency.

Most of all – four pairs of eyes are drawn
towards the garden's lowest point,
a sunken sward of thick new grass,
and growing from that grass a double row
of slender apple-trees – no movement there.

So now the boys make quick their way
towards the shelter of the outer wall.

Thick and grey, its dry-stone dyking of
the highest quality, stands five feet high,
just higher by two inches than their tallest,
but so compacted that no foot of theirs
will dislodge even one small stone
when they come to climb it.

William goes up first, half lifted,
there to squat and act as lookout boy.

    Cry 'showtie' if you see a nun.

Then Stuart scrambles up, pushed from below
his little brother tugging at his sleeve.
Then Rocky, then Harry, pick their holds with care,
peep over the lip, then kneel, then crouch.

The orchard: in their sights; its fruit,
some bobbing on thin twigs contentedly,
some rested on the long grass on the ground.

Before them now: a short plateau.
Golfgrass-topped in richest green, a corner of raised earth,
neatly squared and bordered by thick planking;
just one step down from where the four now stand.

They set off quick across its top, in order as before.

Even William never makes it to the other side
before his feet break through the layer of grass,
his small weight sinking him ankle-deep
into the hidden sticky soup of shit.

Stuart close behind: up to his thighs.

The older, somewhat heavier, two:
their downward progress halted
only by their outspread arms
that stops the surface rising
to the level of their chests.

This protective film of well-fed greenery
having been so pierced, by so many feet,
the stench it trapped beneath now freely lifts.
And as that vapour hits –
And as with gasps it's drawn into their lungs –
Now see these four small boys:
half swim, half claw, their way out
from the clinging claylike mass,
slipping over the dark wood barricade
that holds the fetid matter in its place.

And as they heave and retch and puke,
all four bent double, putrid fumes
so noxious in their age and density
cause each body of each boy
to react as if poisoned;
convulsing and coughing,
puking liquid or puking air,
anything or nothing, it doesn't matter what,
only the puking matters, expulsion, nothing more
– the boys in retribution have no choice.

And when with aching guts and torn-up throats
they shiver themselves straight again,
without a glance to check if they've been spotted
they up and vault the nearest bit of wall.

No stopping.
No helping of each other to its top.
– They see it.
– They make for it.
– They land on the other side.
A little bruised. A little sore.
But with the wall now gladly at their backs.

And yet – the shit is on them as before.

So as fast as the occasional retch allows
they make for the nearest burn,
and find one, not wide, but tiered
into miniature waterfalls and pools,
and here they sit, in a line,
the Ogilvies below, in order of age,
Rocky up top, clothes on,
the water hardly covering their thighs,
as they try to scrub the shit from their skin,
picking with stick-ends where it has clogged
in the seams of their leather shoes.

Walking slowly home they check each other
from time to time, sniffing shirts, sniffing hair.

> *Aye, you're fine.*
> *But the colour.*
> *We'll say we fell.*
> *In human shit?*
> *It could happen.*
> *All at once?*

And nearing Rocky's house, they split,
and he goes in.

Soon after, out he comes again,
his mother, broom in hand,
slams shut the door behind him.

Off he goes. Strolls the half mile,
his clothes fast stiffened by the sun,
to find out how the others fared.

But before he gets there, sees
the three boys stood out in the yard
stripped naked, standing in a row,
with heads hung low and shoulders hunched,
whilst their mother, standing not too close,
throws bucket after bucket of cold water over them.

And they shiver.
And grow pinker.
And hunch closer.

And the water glistens in the sun.
And Rocky turns and goes the other way.

His home is not a home of cuddles,
leastways not for him.

His father uses a belt – ex-service issue;

The only thing that ever gets through to the boy.

choosing not the tradition of leather,
knowing just how woven jute threads
sting upon contact with skin.

The mother has a besom broom
hung upon the back door's inside face;

The flat of a hand no longer works.

only the broom can beat him to her will
– and she doesn't use the straw end.

On one of the rare occasions when
the boy does go to school,
he finds that certain larger children
don't appear to like him very much.

After they've punched and kicked him for a bit
he stands there quite incredulous,
his surprise not at their abject hate,
for which he could not care less;

   My father hits harder than that

is all he can think to say in smart reply
before he gives a minor demonstration
with his fists.

After which he is left alone
and they receive no further hurt.

He has picked the perfect spot to lay his lines.

The burn there: 2 feet deep and 3 across.
By a series of falls and pools above
the underflow of this small stretch is strong.

But a fish's sense of smell is stronger still.
Just as a shark smells blood and moves in quick,
so a trout knows sweat and stays well clear.

From the bankside he tears a good-sized divot,
then rubs his hands upon the earth
and picks the worms that dangle from the clump.

With skin now cleansed from any smell of his
he unravels his line, stakes it low to each bank
then baits the hooks to trail in the water.

The current pulls the lines out straight
holds them to the middle depth
and keeps each fat worm writhing
whilst ensuring any witty fish
will have to work to catch one.

He can leave it that way for days.

Any trout he hooks will be fixed to that spot,
idling against the flow
and the pull of the line on its mouth.

It will stay just as alive, just as fresh, for ages
so sometimes he doesn't take it straight away.
He knows it is there if he wants it.

Little brown dog, half-grown pup,
narrow bodied, gangle legged,
matted coat, near-naked tail,
struggles to stand from a dry ditch
under the glare of a motorcycle lamp.

A thickset shadow passing between
– relaxes the iris, widens green pupils.

As heavy hands descend through low murmurs,
so the wince, the eyelid flicker,
the body shy, shoulder tense, slow flinch.

Hands cup, cradle, lift;
their delicate inspection,
no obvious breaks, just tender aches,
where a thinness of fur hides discoloration.

And the weakness of its clinging to his arms,
and the unaccounted lightness to its bones,
is placed within the sidecar,
in the footwell,
under oil rags,
in the dark.

And the throbbing of the engine as they go
sends it unseen into sleep.

Weeks pass.

The boy: summoned by his father,
is sure he will be punished – can't think why.
Walks with him a full three miles
till they reach his aunt and uncle's house.

No word is spoken all the way,
stern-lipped & hard-eyed, both.
Not guilty: one – the other: resolute.

The house: behind a twin-pump garage;
small, run by the uncle.
In the front room: many dogs.

>   *If you could have one for your own*
>   *which would it be?*

A stupid question for a boy
who knows the dogs belong to someone else,
points out a smooth-haired dachshund
sitting still upon his auntie's lap;

Because it knows its name
and comes when called
and sits when you tell it
and follows when you go.

– his asked-for explanation to his unexpected choice.

His father's careful nod
  Fetch that one out a while.
and points.

And Rocky goes, and gets down on his knees
and hooks the timid creature out
from underneath the high-backed armless chair.

  Read the tag.

And Rocky does, though fearing it's a test
to catch him, being that he can't read much.
Slides the collar round the narrow neck
and lifts the thin brass rectangle, and reads.

  I AM KIM

At which the dog does nothing,
only shivers further at his touch.

  Read the other side.

And Rocky flips the tag, but does not read.

His skill at recognising text is limited,
still sees letters as letters, shapes as shapes,
though some by repetition have sunk in,
and here, though he can't at this moment speak,
he knows the shape before him is his own address.

Now do his eyes begin at once to ache.
Now do their cups fill up with tears,
drip down his cheeks, his lips, hang from his chin;
the dog – unknowingly anointed.

Later as the three walk home:

> *Neglect that dog just once*
> *I'll take him back.*

The boy nods, knowing well he would,
but knowing too
how such will never be.

With a little of the money he makes of times
from the selling of rabbits
or the occasional freshly dead trout,
he has bought himself a knife.

It is a very useful tool, not least
in the eating of *jaggies*, or *tumshies*,
or sometimes potatoes, or carrots; all raw.

He is often hungry and these
are the easiest snack to be had.
Nettles are just as tasty plain as in soup
so long as one knows to avoid being stung.

The knife is not large, its single blade
just two and half inches, hinge to tip,
and half an inch wide at its middle.
The edge folding neatly and stiffly away
into its metal handle, the sides of which
are protected by oblongs of plastic.

The colour of this plastic is tartan.
The line-count matches it to no known clan.
One side of plastic is loose and shifts
ever so slightly about its brass rivets.

Rocky is not allowed, has been forbidden,
to own such an item.
Cannot have it at home.
Cannot have it at school.
Both know he does have it,
force him to turn out his pockets and shoes
on a fairly regular basis.
Never find it.

At the back of the longnose bus
Rocky sits in his usual seat,
dog Kim lying at his feet.

It is the same bus he always gets;
the only bus available.

Split-screen front – cream edges.
The name: MACBRAYNES, in gold upon its side.
    Lime-green roof.
    Long red bonnet.
    Fat black fenders.
    Registration: KGD 903

As he sits he carves his name
into the wooden backing of the chair in front.

Though not fond of letters he does a neat job.

When finished he folds down the blade,
easing it into the handle,
not letting it snap of a sudden shut.

Then he pushes it through a hole
in the red vinyl upholstery of that chair,
deep inside the armrest till he's sure
the padding holds it firm,
is sure it won't slip out.

He stands as the bus slows,
as it nears the stop for the school.
As he stands, so Kim stands,
follows him sure-footed down the aisle.

If quick with the register he'll be able
to catch the bus going the other way,
but it doesn't always turn out so perfectly.

Many years later that very same bus
(many years later the whole MacBraynes fleet)
will be removed from service,
and a young man helping to refurbish the interior
of this particular 1952 Bedford J2 Duple Coach
will find the knife in the very same spot
in which it was so often hidden.

Rusted single blade. Stiff hinge.
One side of plastic a little loose about its pins.

For use on his paper-rounds, and
by need of the gap between houses thereat,
he has made himself a buggy, a guider.

Little more than a platform, with wheels
that he took from a pram; solid vulcanite tyres.
Space enough for himself to stand
with the sack of papers before him,
has to get the balance of weight just right.

The crossbar and pole doesn't steer,
is merely a thing to hold on to,
edging left or right by shifts of position
– does not work so well on sharp corners
– is a burden when going up hill.

For Christmas each of the Ogilvie boys
is given a bicycle – fitted for size.
Sleek wheels with tight new Dunlop valves,
and narrow padded seats, and little bells.

Perfect for the quiet roads of Skye.

So Rocky over several weeks
seeks out and finds the parts to build his own.
Pillaging from buckets before the dustmen come,
scouring every scrap heap; uses mills and lathes
at garages to make or mend the bits he cannot find,
is patient with his chocolate spanners
– all he has as tools to fit it together.

Though Harry's bike is used in consultation to his ends
the finished article resembles nothing
that has ever been before nor ever after.

Back wheel bigger than the front.
A seat that cups both buttocks, not divides.
Handlebars fixed upside down
    (because he thinks that such will make it faster
    and is not surprised to find out that it does).
With racks before and aft to hold
the papers for his round.

Children laugh to see him coming,
often parents join in too, before:

    When will I be able to have
    a better bike than that?

at which all smiles fade.

After months of standard Hebridean weather,
warm rain, dry ice, hard sun, salt wind,
with three smart bikes deposited,
left lying in the yard, with six flat tyres,
Harry wheels his, creaking half a mile

    It won't go, Rocky.
    See what you can make of it.
    I'll let you use the tools it came with.

and leaves it there instead, much safer,
and goes home.

          So Rocky
strips it to its individual parts,
and lays them out upon the grass,
the smaller pieces weighing down
a length of yellow cloth.

With each component picked of rust,
and smoothed and straightened and greased,
he fits it all together and gives it back,
much better now than ever it was before.

In lieu of fees a broken lawnmower
is offered up on his next visit.

> *It's rubbish. It's scrap. It's almost new.*
> *But you'll surely make something of the bits.*

When the slow wind two days later
carries over half a mile the undulating growl
of a small but well-tuned engine,
Mr Ogilvie goes in person,

and standing on the borders of a garden neatly cut
asks above the noise when he can have his mower back.

Some nights away from home he sleeps
beneath the circling panoply of stars –

The dark air under trees: the warmest spot.

And if a chill wind blows then fallen leaves
may serve as blanket, holding back the draught.
And if the warm airs lift and leave the wood
he huddles closer to his dog and both sleep on.

In forty years on winter mornings
when his croft and cars lie cloaked
in films of powdered ice,
the water on his joints will hold him
to the comfort of his bed.

Rising at midday to receive a visitor
he brews fine China tea in a dented pot,
fetches milk and caramel wafers,
tosses two small pitted mats onto the tabletop.

The visitor picks one up –

I like these coasters.

thin rubber discs recycled from old tyres.

Take them.
Can I have six?

He pours the tea;
the gap formed by his thumb and finger
won't close further than an inch-wide hole;
makes holding teapots difficult. He copes;
though work with complex tools will have to wait.

I'll see what I can do.

The visitor gone, he goes outside;
half a jug of grain thrown for his hens;
half a tin of dogfood for each dog.

A copse, a burn, a barbed-wire fence.

Between the water and the bordered field a bank
of tangled grasses, tussocks, lonely trees;
where now the boy walks, easy,
keeping to the middle of that gentle slope.

Kim follows down the darkened line
his rubber-booted feet make
as they knock the silver dewing from
each back-bowed blade of grass.

Mist cloaks the sheep within their field
accentuates their sometime bleats
makes visible the beams of light
the sun, still low, has found to push
through forest holes the mist holds back from sight.

Rocky, hands in pockets, ponders
on the hollow aching of his belly,
has no thought for rabbits, nor for fish,
wanting something ready-made and simple
to appease his gut and plug the ache.

At a point along the burn: a natural pool.
8 feet across, 3 down; calm brownish water.

Here: its distance from the fence is more.
Here: the low bank edging it is flat.

And further on – say, 20 yards – a tree,
up by the fence, tight-laced about its waist
with curls of paper bark in pink and grey.

One hand hooked around the slender trunk,
head back he peers along its centre-line and sees
quite high the tangled shadow of the nest.

He pauses, listens, checks for nearby cawing:
naught but far-off birdsong, water music, sometime bleats.

The quiet is unusual, and yet
the nest is worth a look.

He jumps, hands grip, he starts his climb,
while Kim resigned lies down amidst the roots.

Expert at toe-holds at strength of fingertip
he is not exempt from the tree's own peculiarities.
Its boughs close-knit and thin, his body-squeeze
near frantic scramble through the slightest gap,
ungainly, bending wood with inch-shifts of his weight;
the same inelegance does the trick
in raising him that extra bit,
still nowhere near enough – he stops.

The ascent has been not loud,
tree-creaks and rustled leaves is all;
a heavy wind might do the same or more.
Below he hears the growling of his dog,
and his sharp hush, effective, reminds him
that the dog never speaks without reason.

Following the radar line of Kim's pricked ears
and muzzled point, he spies in the distance – a fox.

Just a fox. Not large.
Red-coated. White tip to the tail. Delicate snout.
Trowel ears that pivot freely as it goes.

No way of telling at such a way
if a vixen or a dog – no matter;
he watches from his height as Kim
quite calm and still, observes below.

The fox keeps close to the fence-line.
It trots easy, pauses, trots on, pauses again.
It doesn't stop at the posts, nor lifts a leg.
Its interest is with the wire.
It carries something in its mouth.
Sometimes when busy at the wire it drops it, momentarily.
Time and distance clarify its business to the watchers.
It is collecting wool.
Where sheep have rubbed against the wire,
stretched their necks for greener grass,
the four-point barbs have snagged upon the fleece.
The fox picks at the hanks the wire's torn out.
It bunches the wool into its jaws.
Mud-white wisps protrude beyond its cheeks.
It works delicately.
Teasing the fibres from the fence.
Adds them to the whole.
Bunches and lifts. Moves on.
When the disordered mass is of
a comparable size to its head, it stops.
It seeks out a bare patch.
Flat earth. Short grass.
It drops the wool and paws it into shape.
Back bent inwards, forelegs straight,
ears cupped forward to the work.
The wool is patted is pressed is clawed is rolled.
The fox's audience: but a dozen yards distance.
Has not yet caught their scent. Is unconcerned.
It stops. It straightens. It stretches. It yawns.
The wool: compacted to the size of a tennisball.
Now gripped between its small front teeth. Tight.
The wool-ball protruding below its black nose.

Only a few strands held within its mouth.
It approaches the burn – the pool – backwards.
At the edge, not looking,
stepping its hind-feet first into the water.
It moves slowly. Deliberately.
It waits a moment; takes more small steps;
each time progressing deeper in.
Its legs – submerged.
The feathers of its tail: free drifting under water.
The waterlevel rising ever further up its body.
Liquid brown, edging up, under wispy red.
Engulfing and darkening.
Currents push each hair up from the skin.
And all the time the ball of wool held high within its teeth.
Until the neck goes under.
Until the ears go under.
The closed eyes. The delicate snout.
Till only a black nose. Flared nostrils.
Then the nose goes too.

And the ball is released.
And away it floats.

Turning and bobbing
out of the pool
and down the burn.

And out comes the fox in a draggle of water.
And sneezes and shakes and goes on its way.

And Rocky knows,
that on that small island of wool
go teeming and crawling and jumping
all of the fleas that before were on the fox.

Shepherds are known to talk of such things.
Though few eyes have ever beheld it.

He watches the ball go bobbing down its course,
kept by the current from touching the sides,
cannot see any sign of movement upon it,
and when at last he looks away
cannot see any sign of the fox.

A letter needs a long gestation;
needs good reason to be writ at all.
Then the writing; the sending; the waiting.

And Rocky's mother picks it from the doormat,
and sighs to see the emblem of the school
stamped firm upon its back, so leaves it for now,
unopened – squarely sat upon the tabletop.

When later on that day the boy comes home,
he is not asked where he has been,
a simple gesture at the letter where it lies,
his recognition of the emblem underneath
the frayed edge of the envelope,
is all that's required.

Next morning – Kim, chained in the yard
watches them lead his master down the road.

Frogmarched to the schoolhouse
up the pathway
through the gate
then left within.

(Though they loiter for a time outside
ensuring that he won't come out again.)

Good morning, Master Rockcliffe.

His teacher;

Just in time.

the principal;

An ideal opportunity.

both smile.

He is led into the big hall.
The other pupils already assembled.
He is led onto the stage, and left.
The principal: his introduction:

> *Since school seems so unworthy of your time,*
> *perhaps you'll be so kind to tell us*
> *what it is you do get up to*
> *when you choose to be elsewhere than here.*

And Rocky, folded arms across his chest,
looks down upon 200 upturned faces,
and lifts his eyes to see the teachers
standing, smiling, waiting, at the back.

So he tells them about the fox.

He tells them everything.
In detail. Start to finish.

His location, his intention, his hunger, the weather, the
water, the long grass, the tree, the climbing, the scratches,
the growling, the hushing, the looking, the fox, its motion,
his stillness, the barbed wire, the wool wisps, collecting,
the pawing, the pool edge, immersion, slow ducking,
its neck, its ears, its eyes, its nose, the release.

And then he explains it.

Pause – Applause.

Not just clapping, but cheering,
some smiles to be seen on the mouths of some teachers,
though each does their best to disguise it.

And Rocky unhindered, unasked, now exits the stage
and makes for the big double doors;
though the groundsman spreadeagles to stop him,
he ducks and slipskids through his legs.

Then down the empty corridor,
then out, then off.

'That began a sad period of his life.
The letters kept on coming.
We kept on marching him back.

And to see the look on his face.
Having to be shut indoors all day.
He couldn't understand it.
It was irrational. Unnatural.

A good thing we all adored Kim.
By our attentions he wasn't neglected.
Suffered little at the lack of his master.'

His newfound popularity at school
has come about by their simply knowing
a tiny bit more about him.

Boys want to follow him.
Girls like to smile as he goes by.

The following's a pain.
He takes it well.
Lets them join him on the odd jaunt.
Achieves little in their company.

The smiles he likes.
He takes them well.
Smiles back and wanders over for a chat.
Most often the smiling-girls run coy away.

He gets called: NATUREBOY
He doesn't mind so much.
It is carelessly done.
Seems vaguely endearing.
He takes it as such.

Whilst standing in line one day
waiting to be let in from the yard,
he hears his name called from a neighbouring line,
and turns and sees another girl, who smiles,
so he smiles back, but doesn't go over.

Her name: MELITA WILSON

A fair-skinned dark-haired thing;
slight of frame; not dressed for the cold;
loves animals and going for long walks;
not fussed about cars; reads often;
is happiest watching seagulls from the cliff-edge;
casting stones into the sea.

When the new-year dance comes round
he asks her to it.
She says YES, and so they go.

Him in his secondhand McKinnon kilt;
her brown hair curled in tresses.

He knows all the dances, all the reels,
is light on his feet and gentles his strength.
Has bought for her a box of Maltesers
– a new thing to be seen upon the isle.
The style of the box attracted him.
Thick matt red cardboard, polka dots in brown.

Cost him no more than a rabbit.
Is sure Melita will be pleased.

Not everyone in school has grown to like him;
a few of his acquaintance hate his guts –
would like to see him beaten to a pulp,
and for that reason mind to stay well clear.

One such: the baker's son.
A cream-faced boy with round blue eyes.
About as big as Rocky
though composed of different stuff.

Come evening he has access to the produce
that his father could not sell and cannot keep.
The sugared items being more expensive,
both to make and to buy,
don't last long behind the counter,
yet it's anything-with-custard he likes best.

No need for dark-houred visits to the shop,
his mother's glad enough if food's not wasted;
a white-iced bun placed in his luncheon box:
a little stale – the glacéed fruit goes first.

For his birthday he's given a rifle,
standard .22 calibre, the bang no more
than a single sharp clap of the hands.

The delight of the present brings tears to his eyes.

Regularly strips and oils it; unloaded at night
it is propped by his bed as he sleeps, with three bullets
folded into a cloth, tucked under his pillow.

At weekends he can be seen on the heath
popping rabbits from a distance of 40 yards.
He only ever sees their sudden downward drop,
no need to collect – leaves the carcase for crows,
does not seek out thanks from the crofters.

With that rifle, some years later,
he will shoot Kim clean through the head,
though none will say for certain it was him.

Sport, as every other lesson, is compulsory.

It is character building.
It promotes team-man-ship.
It is a source of much needed exercise.
It is fun.

In a game of football, Rocky is placed in goal.

Whilst his side is winning the ball is no more
than a small white dot at the far end of the field,
occasionally glimpsed in the air, on the ground,
in the gaps between a bustle of puffing bodies,
and the squirming gangly motion of their legs.

A couple of defenders stand halfway between,
static, chatting to each other, about girls,
about radio shows, about anything but the game;
they jump to keep warm; one of them spits.

Then the tide turns for the opposition,
and the white dot grows, bringing with it
all the bustle and noise and anger and fun
down to this end of the makeshift pitch.

The defenders tense and dance upon the spot
in readiness, and one of them (the one who spat)
gets in a lucky kick and boots the ball
and the crowd and the shouting and the mud
back towards the other end again.

And the wind sighs.
And the birds resume their song.

And Rocky, hands in pockets,
wanders from the goalmouth
off into the woods and out of sight.

In later days his father
has a part-time job with BUPA
Mostly dealing with deliveries.

Just as strong as in his youth;
at need can carry coffins on his back.

On arriving at Edinburgh to collect,
and on giving his name at reception,
the girl behind the desk looks up and starts.

>*Mr Rockcliffe?*
>*Aye, that's me.*
>*You wouldn't know a Rocky, by chance?*
>*Aye, that's my son.*

She brushes a strand of long dark hair
behind a small pink ear and bites her lip.

>*Would you give him a message?*

He nods.
She writes her number on a Post-It note.

>*My name's Melita Wilson.*
>*Rocky was my first ever boyfriend.*
>*It's possible he won't remember me.*

He nods. He does not smile.
An expression altogether hard to read.
No recognition. No surprise. Nothing to say.

He takes the pallid yellow slip
and promises to pass it on.

'It wasn't a very long phonecall,
maybe 10 mins at the most;
he called as soon as he got the number.

I told him of my work.
He said he couldn't tell me much of his.

It turned out that I'd been his first,
just as he'd been to me.
That before that dance I'd never been kissed,
that neither had he.

It wasn't awkward, just as when young
he was so very easy to talk to.
But under the press of all those years,
we didn't have much to say.

So I thanked him again for the Maltesers.
Told him that I'd liked them very much.'

The Ogilvie boys:
back from holidaying in Lyon.

Their *oui monsieur*,
their *s'il vous plaît*,
their *lait au menthe, merci*.

And Rocky cannot help but be impressed;
not so much by the words themselves
– at their deliverance.

The confident pomposity.
The air of self-importance.
The swaggered sun-tanned smile.

Decides he has to try this for himself.

So in the evening he checks his father's globe.
And in the night he dreams of different worlds.
Then in the morning goes.

His hessian satchel/sack, now partly filled
with biscuit, all that he could find – not much.
In his pocket a purse of little coinage
as well as a ten-shilling note, folded,
and sealed inside a cashier's see-through bag.
Then thinking how in France it may be hot
a pair of plastic sandals – green;
squeaking brightly on his naked feet.

And that is all he carries for his trip;
that and the clothes he stands up in:
his shorts, his jumper two sizes too big.

Come dawn he pats his dog goodbye
then walks the four short miles to Portree.

Conservation of funds is not a concern,
has dodged the ferry fare before,
and at the mainland station
just a penny platform ticket –
all he needs to get him to the capital.

His mistake in getting off the train
at Haymarket and not at Waverley
gives him opportunity to exercise his legs.
Does not dawdle in the gardens,
merely glances at the castle up above,
his purpose not with them, just passing through.

The manner of his getting all the way down to King's Cross
is just as before.

The 1st class carriages – so rarely occupied,
he picks an empty compartment, leaves the door ajar,
and hearing footsteps above the steady rumble of the train
squeezes himself into the gap between seat-back and wall.

Plenty of space to lie down once in,
though of times he is careless,
and dozes, and is caught.

Amidst tears and protestations of desertion and of loss,
his punishment: to be dropped at the next stop;
not really the conductor's concern beyond that.
So Rocky waits an hour or so
then catches the train that comes after.

Hitching out of London to the port
he surveys the situation now at hand.

Perched upon a concrete mooring post
and eating the last of his biscuit he watches
the schoolchildren herded up onto the boat
– then slips unseen into their midst.

So many children from so many schools
nobody questions his presence, becoming
just one more head to be counted.

Whilst crossing – he takes his meals with them,
and quietly is more heartfelt in his grace.
At Calais – he eyes the turnstile, slips through
with a group that should have numbered eight.
On the train – he wanders, deliberately,
and gestures at need to guards he's with the school.

But in Paris
such cover goes quickly.

He spends a lot of time in the main station,
by day doesn't stray far from its bounds.
Observing the manners of tramps he collects
his own cardboard box from outside a shop
and come nighttime positions it carefully
above the thin steel grilles set in the floor,
through which the warm air from the metro blows.

For safety his 10-bob note he hides
in the narrow space between two walls,
in a hole, beneath a brick,
is sure nobody sees him.
The coins: changed into francs.
Not amounting to much.
Won't last long.

One thing he never counted on:
the overwhelming pleadings of his gut.

Lingering each morning by the boulevard cafés
he fills up on leftover morsels of croissant
and drains a dozen cups of coffee dregs;
he doesn't like the taste but takes
whatever he can get –
if lucky, a mouthful of butter or jam;
the waitresses don't stop him –
unsmiling they smile at what is not left to clean up.

With his purse at last quite empty
and no thought of what to do next
he phones the embassy.

Not easy without money or language.
Three seconds after getting the switchboard
and the lady's *oui monsieur* the line goes dead.
With repeated efforts and a single digit
spoken loud each time the lady takes the call,
the phonebooth's number is completed
and she rings him back.

According to the embassy man
because the boy's visit to France
is of a voluntary nature
there's nothing they can do to help.
He suggests: that Rocky writes his destination
large upon a piece of card
then stands and prays for kindness to get home.

Rocky thanks him for the tip
and hangs up.

The quiet cobble of the streets
away from Paris' middle town
is far more to his liking.
He carries a torn-off flap of his box.
He borrows a pen from a grunting poet
drunk on the fumes from walnut wine.
At the city limits, by the roadside,
he holds up his silent request
it says: LYON

A native family going that way
pick him up, and do not mind
that all he can say is *thankyou*.

The journey drags. He falls asleep.
Unknowingly, the cushion for his head
– the daughter's lap.

Ten years his senior, she doesn't mind;
gazes out the window all the while.

The heat of Lyon: hotter than he had expected.
By the evening of the first day
the seams of his plastic shoes have melted
and they fall apart.

It is a small matter.
He sees how most around him go barefoot.
He does likewise.

But his problem now is the same as in Paris:
a penetrative hunger
that scrounging in crowded places never seems to satisfy.

Nipping from table to table
at an outdoor wedding reception
he is watched.

A tall thin man in a crumpled linen suit,
long pale hair, delicate bony fingers,
has taken particular interest
in the diminutive stranger's cautious antics;
has observed the pinkness of that tender skin,
has noticed too his shoeless double limp;
at length approaches him, gently,
smiling, non-threatening, crouches,
as the boy gnaws on a chicken-leg –
a sticky profiterole clutched in his other hand.

He talks in English, has an English accent,
asks the boy if he is English too. The answer:

    No.
    I live on Skye.

The man's name is Fairy.
He is not a homosexual.
A beatnik from St Ives whose girlfriend
lives in France (because she's French)
where for the moment he has joined her
whilst the music festivals play out.

The girlfriend lives nearby,
her house upon the outskirts of Lyon.
She is tall and wispish,
just like her house,
just like Fairy,
with fragile qualities of face and frame;
like gossamer her straw-blonde hair
that with the slightest breath is made to float.

Her first resolve, past greeting him,
to check the soles of Rocky's feet.
Through her pained frowns, her murmurs, her wincing,
she bathes them in cool yellow water
from a chipped unsteady porcelain bowl,
while Rocky, careless, eats the bread
and wine and cheese they've given him.

Next morning without improvement the trio
travel to the local hospital –
the boy with three of the girlfriend's
thin grey socks upon each foot.

And the doctor, through mutters and squints,
as he bandages the blackened skin,
in serious tone commands the boy to

    Never do a thing like this again.

– and Rocky promises he never will.

Just as a wounded animal seeks out
the place where it is most at peace,
so all that Rocky thinks of now
is getting back to Skye.

As such, whilst staying in the modest squalor
of the Frenchgirl's house, the boy is found
a pair of leather sandals, big enough
to fit over his knee-length bandages.
And Fairy asks around and pools
enough to buy a ticket back to Paris,
from where, the boy assures them,
he will have no problem getting home.

And the first thing he does
on arriving at that city station
is to find the gap between two walls,
then the hole, then the loose brick,
and retrieve his 10-bob note from where
he hid it for safe keeping.

For extra special caution
(for he knows not what might happen next)
the note is hid again,
upon his person;
its plastic wrappings proving now most useful.

The rest is easy.

It is still high summer.
Plenty of schools pass forth and back
across the English Channel.

And his arrival back in Dover
calls for solitary celebration,
first with the removal of his hidden paper note,
then with the purchase
of one portion
of egg and chips.

Of course he's been away from home before.
Some nights he will sleep beneath the countless stars.
But two weeks without word
nor explanation for his walking out the door,
has been too much to bear.

The manhunt that scoured the isle
turned up neither body nor trace
– no one knew a thing of where he was.

Needless to say when through the yard he walks,
and after the frantic lickings of his dog,
not a soul believes his having been in France.
For one, as his mother points out,
he doesn't have a passport.

But punishments are duly restrained
in view of unknown damage to his legs.

Next morning, to the doctor: Dr Black

– whose initial observation
said with quiet surprise, is that
the bandages are French.

And as he checks the sores beneath.
And as he ascertains they're healing well.
And as he wraps them in fresh lint, he says:

Don't ever do a thing like that again.

And Rocky never does, although
he cannot help but think upon
the wider possibilities
his opened world presents.

Of times he can be found down at the garage
as attendant for the pumps.

Too young to be employed
they yet soon tire of chasing him off –
he only comes back again.

The little that by choice they pay him
is in due deference to his persistence.

Tell you what, Rocky,
you fix up that old car there,
you can keep it.

– a 1937 Riley-9 saloon. In burgundy.
The challenge is merely to keep him
from under their feet.

For a couple of weeks their plan works.

Until he fixes the car,
and takes it home,
then comes back to the pumps.

In quite a different quarter of the island
from the boundings of the convent
– a hospital.

In fact a big grey house: a mansion: a castle.

Mrs Ogilvie works there.
Has explained how it's not a regular hospital.
Has not described the patients it admits.

Occasionally, whilst tramping through its gardens,
the boys chance to spot one, standing,
just a little way down from –
a little way beyond the edge of –
the house's smoothly tiered lawn;
dressed in a floral dressing-gown,
with very little underneath,
as hinted at by lazy puffs of wind.

Just standing, bare-foot,
toes dividing blades of uncut grass,
one hand loosely clasping closed the gown,
the other fingering the rim of an earlobe,
and smiling, smiling such a smile,
for no one, for the nothing being stared at,
that surpasses all the densities of earth.

Till the matron who has lived a million years
comes to escort the patient back indoors,
and gives the children such a glare
that says: GET OUT OR I SHALL HAVE YOU KILLED.

And duly they back off – but do not leave.

In the farthest corner of the grounds
where the topmost turret of the house
can just be glimpsed,
there stands a dragon-tree.

A gnarly trunk from which a cone
of branches upward spreads, top-heavy,
not a single leaf
until the round green plateau of its top.

Not easy to climb,
can only be properly viewed
by shinning up the normal trees
that stand protective nearby.

But that round green top –
perfect as a platform, as a lookout,
though without some wooden reinforcements
probably would not support
the boys' composited weight.

As such a pulley system is devised:
a steel bar through the centre
of a tyreless metal wheel;
a sash cord from a washing line
set in the narrow groove;
and various planks of wood are hoisted up,
as well as other oddments.

And when the work is nearly through
there is a wondering amongst them all
of whether Harry can be hoisted too,
because it would be useful
to have him first up top.

He is tall, but not broad, and the cord
has proved itself quite strong. They try.

And though the fibres
    creak against the weight they have to pull –
And though the steel bar
    jammed in the branches starts to bend –
And though the knot
    grows tighter and his sides begin to ache –

All proceeds just fine.
Until all stops proceeding fine.

And the sash cord snaps and spins back through the wheel.
And the bar springs up and clatters from the tree.
And Harry falls and crumples to the grass.

The other three get slowly up
from where they too have fallen,
and inspect the body that doesn't move,
that doesn't respond to its name when called,
that appears overly floppy when shaken.

After some short and careful debate
the most popular solution: to bury him
and swear when asked that they know nothing
of Harry's whereabouts.

It is almost agreed upon,
though William, by his age,
cannot be trusted to keep such a secret;
is bound by accident to let it slip.

Instead they choose to lift him up –
Rocky the legs, Stuart the arms.

That floppiness again, now more pronounced.
The legs not bending in the way they should.
The right shoulder not as solid as the left.

They carry him up to the hospital,
and place him down upon the big front step,
and check by sight that he at least still breathes;
then ring the bell,
then run.

One final glance back
from the safety of the border wall,
and small in the distance they spy
the square hole of the opened front door,
and in it the ancient matron,
and Mrs Ogilvie,
with the stillness of the body at their feet,
and no one else around.

One month, two months,
and Harry is allowed outside again,
and his brothers go with him as ever.

Though forbidden, they meet up with Rocky.

It is high summer.
Harry is in a wheelchair while he mends.
An iron-shod pre-war thing.

Those few weeks,
riding Harry's chair,
down quiet island roads,
the best that they have known.

Come autumn,
Harry goes to boarding school,
on the mainland;
is rarely seen in the holidays.

Mr Ogilvie opens up a chain of sandwich bars.
The ones in Edinburgh being so successful,
it's not so long before he owns
all the sandwich bars in Rose Street.

Many years later Rocky chances
to find himself in one of them
being approached unknown from behind
when he hears:

> *How you doing, Rocky.*

and turns to see a massive man,
six-foot five and a thumb,
50-inch chest,
melon-headed,
with button-blue eyes,
who turns out to be William.

And Rocky's

> *How'd you ken it was me?*

is answered first
by a shrug
then a sniff
then a smile
then –

> *Because you still smell of shit.*

That letter of apology
to the matron of the castle/hospital
– the worst punishment he has ever received.

The effort of turning the words in his head
into shapes for the page
then to trace out each line with his pen,
has him weeping in anguish,
is acutely painful
for his fingers, for his eyeballs, for his throat.

But after several hours he's done,
and from it learns
to be more careful next time round.

'He was too old to mess around in class.
In ways – he was my star pupil.

He came to me explaining his problem with words.
But he was determined.
He'd paid for it too.

It's one thing to speak the Gaelic
– quite another to write or read it.

And when one boy who wasn't there by choice
started laughing from the back,
Mr Rockcliffe turning (from the front)
tells him: to shut the bleep up, or get the bleep out.
Though without the bleeps – of course.

They became good friends after that.
That is – I saw them chatting once or twice.'

In the first year of the new century
at a car convention
for vehicles made early in the last,
he sees his old schoolbus.

Sat back from the rest on the edge of the show
the blue island water behind it
and all its red and black and lime and cream
gleaming as if new – or else
just cleaned and polished and placed under a high sun.

He speaks to the current owner proud beside it.
They talk of engine size, of torque ratios;
a subject he had never linked it with before.

He tells about his knife and how
the bus was the only hideaway
that could be trusted to keep the secret.

The details are noted down in the logbook
and he learns how during restoration
a knife was actually found,
and shown around and puzzled at,
then thrown away as junk.

He steps aboard,
and knows he does not recognise
the slight sag of the bus
beneath his tripled weight.

Alone he makes his way along the aisle, and sits;
back seat, corner seat, his seat,
with no dog now to lie still at his feet.

The arm-rest – no hole,
with all its stuffing tight beneath
its new red vinyl skin.

But on the upright backing of the chair,
the wood so newly oiled and waxed
still bears the name of ROCKY carved
quite neatly through its narrow grain.

He chooses not to mention this when he steps off,
just thanks the man and walks away.

A hot and clammy day on Skye.
Sweat beading underneath his canvas shorts.

He removes his shoes, his socks.
Takes to walking in the burn itself.
Ensuring any scent of his won't linger on the grass.
Has no mind for fish today.

And Kim without waiting for a word,
steps into the shallow water too,
and follows in the rippled beer-brown wake.

Just as any other wounded beast,
seeking out the spot
where it feels most at peace,
so ten years later whilst Rocky is mending
a carburettor in the garage shop,
Kim comes and lies down at his feet
and does not move.

And oil-covered hands inspect his head
and find the tiny hole the bullet made
and touch upon the tiny gleam of blood
matted in the brown hairs over his eye.

Big man, big tears;
from cheek to chin to dog;
with Kim – unknowingly anointed.

And next morning when his mother goes
to buy her groceries, the baker's wife
will not accept her payment for the goods.

Nothing more is said of it than that;
the matter is dropped.

Rocky will never discuss it;
of no concern to anyone but him,
of little concern at all;
just a boy and his dog,
one following the other up the burn,
no words between them – no need.

'I was never soft with the boy.
Where would that have got him?

He mayn't have been the brightest spark at school,
but three days after he came back
from circling the globe,
I went to his garage and shook his hand.

It took him long enough.
He stopped in several countries on the way.
Though it must be said: in all that time,
he never set a foot in France again.'

And in a long-forgotten drawer
beneath an oak-cased gramophone,
the only certificate he's ever had:
for swimming – bronze award.

(B) editions

www.cbeditions.com